Catching On

Motivational Activities in Reading Comprehension

Workbook I

Valerie Anderson, Carl Bereiter, Douglas Raisbeck, David Smart

Open Court
La Salle, Illinois

OPEN COURT and ❄ are registered in the
U.S. Patent and Trademark Office.

Copyright © 1987, 1983 Open Court Publishing Company

Printed in the United States of America

ISBN 0-89688-915-7

Circle the picture that goes with the sentence.

The goat is eating a birthday cake.

Circle the picture that goes with the sentence.

A monkey played the drums.

Mark the best answer to each question. The first one is done for you.

1. Which is biggest? ☐

    ____ your eye

    ____ your hand

    ✓ your head

2. Which is smallest? ☐

    ____ a house

    ____ a hat

    ____ a horse

3. Which goes fastest? ☐

    ____ a car

    ____ a frog

    ____ a child

4. Which moves most slowly? ☐

    ____ a deer

    ____ a worm

    ____ a jet

5. Which is thinnest? ☐

    ____ a shoelace

    ____ a thread

    ____ a rope

6. Which is hardest? ☐

    ____ an apple

    ____ a rubber ball

    ____ a sidewalk

7. Which is loudest? ☐

    ____ a watch

    ____ a horn

    ____ a mouse

CHECK: Read each question and the answers again. Did you think about all three things before you marked the best answer?

Underline the best word to complete each sentence. Then print that word in the blank. The first one is done for you.

1. Boots keep feet _____dry_____. ☐

    small   brave   <u>dry</u>

2. Dogs like to chew _____. ☐

    bones   clouds   air

3. You can see through _____. ☐

    sidewalks   windows   bones

4. The teacher rang the school _____. ☐

    room   bell   book

5. We crossed the lake in a _____. ☐

    sail   boat   fish

6. At noon we eat our _____. ☐

    breakfast   table   lunch

<u>CHECK</u>: Read each completed sentence. Does it make sense? Does the word you chose sound right with the rest of the sentence?

Read each question. Then print a word in the blank to complete the answer. The first one is done for you.

1. Which is it—an arm, an ankle, or an eye?

   It's part of the head, so it must be an ___eye___. ☐

2. Which is it—a lunch, a truck, or a pole?

   It has wheels, so it must be a _____. ☐

3. Which is it—shoes, meat, or hats?

   People eat it, so it must be _____. ☐

4. Which is it—a river, a rug, or a cloud?

   You walk on it, so it must be a _____. ☐

5. Which is it—a pencil, a spoon, or a mop?

   You clean with it, so it must be a _____. ☐

6. Which is it—a bus, a tree, or a house?

   You ride on it, so it must be a _____. ☐

7. Which is it—a goat, a dog, or a snake?

   It has horns, so it must be a _____. ☐

CHECK: Read each completed sentence. Does it make sense?

Synthesis: Solving structured riddles

Mark the silly sentence. The first one is done for you.

1. ✓ The door chased the rabbit.
   ____ The dog chased the rabbit.

2. ____ The salt was on the table.
   ____ The sky was on the table.

3. ____ Many people drink milk.
   ____ Many people drink moon.

4. ____ Diane ate the books.
   ____ Diane ate the bread.

5. ____ The farm liked to run.
   ____ The horse liked to run.

6. ____ Fish live in that lake.
   ____ Fish live in that tree.

7. ____ The man drove the car.
   ____ The man drove the lake.

CHECK: Read each sentence you did not mark.
It should make sense.

Follow the directions. Draw on the picture only what each direction tells you to draw.

1. Draw a neck on the woman. ☐

2. Draw two eyebrows. ☐

3. Draw round earrings on the woman's ears. ☐

4. Draw a necklace around the woman's neck. ☐

CHECK: Read each direction again. Then look at your picture. Did you do what the direction told you to do?

Read each direction. Draw on the picture only what each direction tells you to draw.

1. Draw a tail on the dog. ☐

2. Draw two ears on the dog. ☐

3. Draw a collar around the dog's neck. ☐

4. Draw three large spots on the dog. ☐

CHECK: Read each direction again. Then look at your picture. Did you do what the direction told you to do?

Underline the things you need to draw to finish this head. Then draw them.

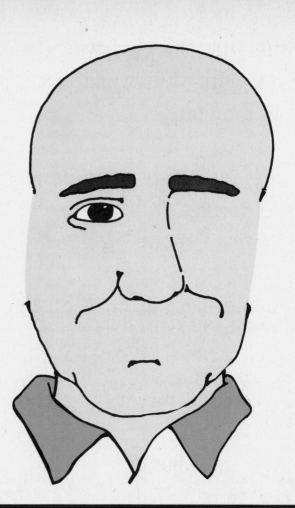

a tail   eyelashes

a shoe   ears

a nose   a mouth

two feet   a leg

hair   an arm

one eye   an eyebrow

Using imagery: Identifying the missing parts of a drawing

Circle the picture that goes with the sentence.

The turtle danced with a cane.

Using imagery: Selecting a picture to illustrate a sentence

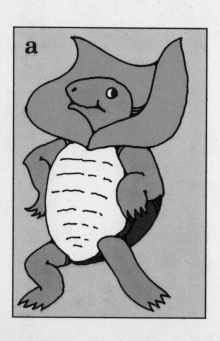

a

b

c

Underline the best word to complete each sentence. Then print that word in the blank. The first one is done for you.

1. People wash their hands with
   _____soap_____. □
   soup   <u>soap</u>   gloves

2. June wore a mask on her _____. □
   coat   hide   face

3. We stick papers together with
   _____. □
   glue   pencils   bread

4. People can fly in a _____. □
   plane   bird   boat

5. The color of most grass is _____. □
   gray   cut   green

6. Peas roll because they are
   _____. □
   round   tasty   green

CHECK: Read each completed sentence. Does it make sense? Does the word you chose sound right with the rest of the sentence?

8

Determining meaning from context: Using context *before* a blank

Mark the best answer to each question. The first one is done for you.

1. Which is sharpest? ☐

_____ a crayon

_____ a spoon

✓ a nail

2. Which is hottest? ☐

_____ your arm

_____ a fire

_____ a stick

3. Which is tallest? ☐

_____ a person

_____ an elephant

_____ an ant

4. Which is softest? ☐

_____ a pillow

_____ your head

_____ a brick

5. Which is wettest? ☐

_____ a river

_____ a house

_____ a coat

6. Which is smoothest? ☐

_____ a rug

_____ a road

_____ a glass

7. Which is longest? ☐

_____ a cat

_____ a horse

_____ a dog

CHECK: Read each question and the answers again. Did you think about all three things before you marked the best answer?

Circle the picture that goes with the sentence.

Marco waved a flower.

Using imagery: Selecting a picture to illustrate a sentence

Underline the things you need to draw to finish this elephant. Then draw them.

Using imagery: Identifying the missing parts of a drawing

an arm	a mouth
one ear	a tail
a coat	two eyes
a trunk	a hat
a foot	a neck
toenails	a back

10

Mark the silly sentence. The first one is done for you.

1. _____ Mike ate his stew with a spoon. □

    ✓ Mike ate his stove with a spoon.

2. _____ The cows lived on the fence. □

    _____ The cows lived on the farm.

3. _____ I always carry a comb for my hair. □

    _____ I always carry a crumb for my hair.

4. _____ Murray kept his money in his water. □

    _____ Murray kept his money in his wallet.

5. _____ She cut the bread with a sharp knife. □

    _____ She cut the bread with a sharp shoe.

6. _____ Do you hear that cloud ticking? □

    _____ Do you hear that clock ticking?

7. _____ Grace picked peaches off the tree. □

    _____ Grace picked beaches off the tree.

CHECK: Read each sentence you did <u>not</u> mark.
It should make sense.

Underline the best word to complete each sentence.
Then print that word in the blank.

1. The woods are full of _____. □

   cars   buildings   trees

2. After dinner I go to _____. □

   lunch   sleep   school

3. Many people see wild animals in

   _____. □

   schools   farms   zoos

4. Wilma is in class reading a _____. □

   book   pen   bone

5. Sam cools off by taking cold

   _____. □

   soap   showers   naps

6. Never play with _____! □

   fire   cats   flowers

7. The man mowed the _____. □

   street   table   lawn

CHECK: Read each completed sentence. Does it make
sense? Does the word you chose sound right with the
rest of the sentence?

Determining meaning from context: Using context before a blank

Mark the silly sentence. Then circle the word that makes it silly. The first one is done for you.

1. ✓ The net catches (stars.) □
   ___ The net catches fish.

2. ___ Nancy read the book. □
   ___ Nancy read the egg.

3. ___ The plate had food on it. □
   ___ The rain had food on it.

4. ___ Sally ate a big desk. □
   ___ Sally ate a big dinner.

5. ___ They ride to school in a bus. □
   ___ They ride to school in a bump.

6. ___ Taro built a house yesterday. □
   ___ Taro buttered a house yesterday.

7. ___ He wrote a letter with a pan. □
   ___ He wrote a letter with a pen.

CHECK: Read each sentence you did <u>not</u> mark. It should make sense.

Recognizing whether text makes sense: Identifying absurd sentences

Underline the best word to complete each sentence.
Then print that word in the blank.

1. _____ bring thunder

   Storms   Stores   Worms

   and lightning. ☐

2. _____ can grow in flowerpots. ☐

   Saws   Woods   Weeds

3. _____ should not be passed on. ☐

   Songs   Secrets   Help

4. _____ grows on top of your head. ☐

   A hat   Hair   Ice

5. _____ can start fires. ☐

   Pennies   Water   Matches

6. _____ are used to lock doors and

   Buttons   Keys   Tires

   start cars. ☐

CHECK: Read each completed sentence. Does it make
sense? Does the word you chose sound right with the
rest of the sentence?

14

Mark the sentence that goes with the picture.

_____ A bear rode on a goat.

_____ A goat rode on a bear.

Circle the picture that goes with the sentence.

The pig answered the telephone.

Mark the best answer to each question.

1. Which is fattest? ☐

_____ a worm

_____ a snake

_____ a pig

2. Which is thinnest? ☐

_____ a pencil

_____ a needle

_____ a baseball bat

3. Which is shortest? ☐

_____ a doll

_____ a child

_____ a flag pole

4. Which is fastest? ☐

_____ a plane

_____ a bike

_____ a tractor

5. Which is driest? ☐

_____ an ice cube

_____ a lake

_____ a corn flake

6. Which is stickiest? ☐

_____ sand

_____ honey

_____ salt

7. Which is sweetest? ☐

_____ a lemon

_____ a carrot

_____ a candy cane

CHECK: Read each question and the answers again. Did you think about all three things before you marked the best answer?

Semantic ordering: Answering superlative questions

Read each sentence. Then follow the directions to answer a question about the sentence. Print your answer in the blank. The first one is done for you.

1. **Carla gave Norm an alligator.**
   Print <u>one</u> <u>word</u> from the sentence.
   Who gave the alligator away? _____ *Carla* _____ □

2. **Dirk took out carrots and ate them.**
   Print <u>one</u> <u>word</u> from the sentence.
   What did Dirk eat? _____ □

3. **The children lost the king's yo-yo today.**
   Print <u>one</u> <u>word</u> from the sentence.
   When was the yo-yo lost? _____ □

4. **Zelda taught her mouse some new tricks.**
   Print <u>one</u> <u>word</u> from the sentence.
   Who taught the mouse tricks? _____ □

5. **Gene put ribbons on his pet mouse.**
   Print <u>one</u> <u>word</u> from the sentence.
   What did Gene put on his pet mouse? _____ □

<u>CHECK</u>: Read each question and the word you printed. Does the word make a good answer to the question?

Follow the directions. Draw on the picture only what each direction tells you to draw.

1. Draw a square hat on the elephant's head. □

2. Draw a ring around the end of its trunk. □

3. Draw a square blanket on its back. □

4. Draw an X at the end of its tail. □

CHECK: Read each direction again. Then look at your picture. Did you do what the direction told you to do?

Follow the directions, and finish the picture. Then answer the question. Print your answer in the blank.

1. Draw a line from **a** to **b.**

2. Draw a line from **c** to **d.**

What did you draw? _____

Mark the sentence that goes with the picture.

_____ The pig painted the house.

_____ The pig painted the horse.

Underline the things you need to draw to finish this turtle. Then draw them.

a trunk	a belt	a neck
two eyes	a leg	two wings
fur	a head	a tail
a shell	a belly	a mouth

Follow the directions, and finish the picture.

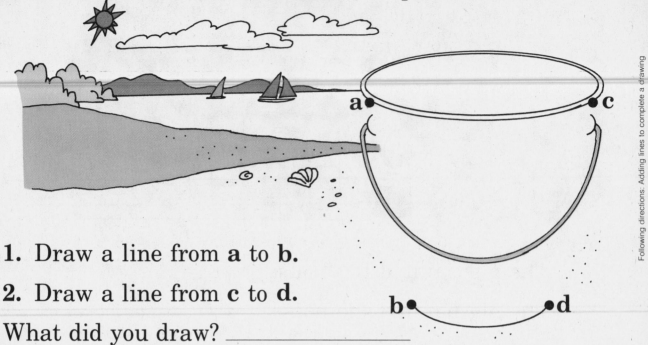

1. Draw a line from **a** to **b**.
2. Draw a line from **c** to **d**.

What did you draw? _____

Follow the directions, and finish the picture.

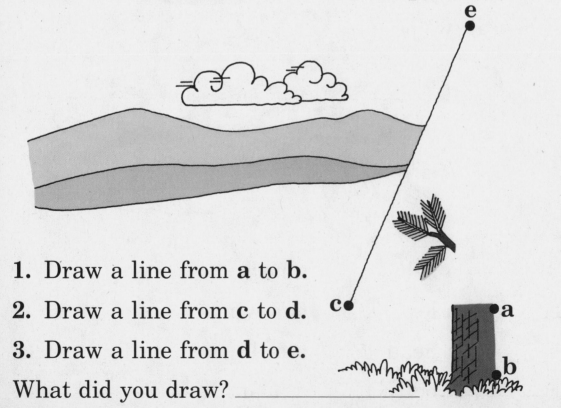

1. Draw a line from **a** to **b**.
2. Draw a line from **c** to **d**.
3. Draw a line from **d** to **e**.

What did you draw? _____

Underline the things you
need to draw to finish this
baseball player. Then draw them.

a mouth   a baseball bat

a T-shirt   a belt

a nose   two eyebrows

a cup   a leg

a shoe   a tail

a tongue   an eye

Circle the picture that goes with the sentence.

The broom held the salt shaker.

Using imagery: Identifying the missing parts of a drawing

Using imagery: Selecting a picture to illustrate a sentence

Mark the silly sentence. Then circle the word that makes it silly.

1. ____ The bag was full of schools. ☐

   ____ The bag was full of balls.

2. ____ The child ran across the room. ☐

   ____ The chair ran across the room.

3. ____ Horses eat wood in the summer. ☐

   ____ Horses eat grass in the summer.

4. ____ The fish sings a pretty song. ☐

   ____ The bird sings a pretty song.

5. ____ The wind blows the leaves away. ☐

   ____ The wind blows the stones away.

6. ____ Rosa watered every plant in her room. ☐

   ____ Rosa watered every farm in her room.

7. ____ The girl drank mops with her lunch. ☐

   ____ The girl drank milk with her lunch.

CHECK: Read each sentence you did not mark. It should make sense.

Recognizing whether text makes sense: Identifying absurd sentences

Mark the sentence that goes with the picture.

_____ The fish swam in the pond.

_____ The duck swam in the bathtub.

_____ The duck swam in the pond.

Circle the picture that goes with the sentence.

The rabbit is in the hat.

Underline the best word to complete each sentence. Then print that word in the blank.

1. _____ are homes you

    Apartments   Tents   Arrows

    can move easily. ☐

2. _____ get sore in small shoes. ☐

    Knees   Fingers   Feet

3. _____ get into cupboards. ☐

    Barns   Bugs   Horses

4. _____ have more legs

    Chickens   Snakes   Horses

    than people. ☐

5. _____ balls do not bounce. ☐

    Tennis   Rubber   Flat

6. _____ children need bed rest. ☐

    Loud   Sick   Happy

CHECK: Read each completed sentence. Does it make sense? Does the word you chose sound right with the rest of the sentence?

Determining meaning from context: Using context after a blank

Read each sentence. Then follow the directions to answer a question about the sentence. Print your answer in the blank. The first one is done for you.

1. **Monday was Ted's seventh birthday.**
   Print <u>one</u> <u>word</u> from the sentence.
   When was Ted's seventh birthday? ___Monday___ ☐

2. **Marta is going to watch TV tonight.**
   Print <u>one</u> <u>word</u> from the sentence.
   When is Marta going to watch TV? _____ ☐

3. **Olga kicked the football across the field.**
   Print <u>two</u> <u>words</u> from the sentence.
   What did Olga kick across the field?

   _____ ☐

4. **"Rita owns the fastest frog in town," said Leo.**
   Print <u>one</u> <u>word</u> from the sentence.
   Who owns the fastest frog in town? _____ ☐

5. **Mona watched Lisa stand on her head.**
   Print <u>one</u> <u>word</u> from the sentence.
   Who stood on her head? _____ ☐

<u>CHECK</u>: Read each question and the word you printed. Does the word make a good answer to the question?

Locating answers to questions: Isolating sentence parts as answers

Read each question. Then print a word in the blank to complete the answer. The first one is done for you.

1. Which is it—walls, floors, or rain?

   They hold up the roof, so they must be ___walls___. ☐

2. Which is it—a board, a pool, or a store?

   You swim in it, so it must be a _____. ☐

3. Which is it—a mountain, a shoe, or a ring?

   You wear it on your hand, so it must be a

   _____. ☐

4. Which is it—a bicycle, a bank, or a fork?

   You ride on it, so it must be a _____. ☐

5. Which is it—a floor, a plate, or a window?

   You walk on it, so it must be a _____. ☐

6. Which is it—a mountain, a pool, or a spoon?

   You climb up it, so it must be a _____. ☐

7. Which is it—a book, a pencil, or a plant?

   You water it, so it must be a _____. ☐

CHECK: Read each completed sentence. Does it make sense?

Synthesis: Solving structured riddles

Circle the word that makes the sentence silly. The first one is done for you.

1. Cars, (boats,) and trucks move on wheels. ☐

2. Bread, fruit, sidewalks — they taste good. ☐

3. Horses, snakes, and worms have no legs. ☐

4. Eagles, pigs, and owls have feathers. ☐

5. Tubs, pencils, and jars can hold water. ☐

6. Cake, lemons, and limes taste sour. ☐

7. Snow, fires, and ice feel cold. ☐

8. Houses, cars, streets, and schools all have roofs. ☐

Recognizing whether text makes sense: Identifying misclassified items in sentences

CHECK: Read each sentence without the word you circled. It should make sense.

Underline the best word to complete each sentence.
Then print that word in the blank.

1. _____ may be used instead of glue. ☐
   Tap   Tape   Paper

2. Many _____ grow underground. ☐
   roots   leaves   rocks

3. Drinking _____ makes you sick. ☐
   juice   paint   milk

4. _____ are not horse food. ☐
   Grass   Hay   Pork chops

5. _____ help some people
   Gloves   Eyeglasses   Beards

   see better. ☐

6. _____ let light into my room. ☐
   Walls   Rugs   Windows

CHECK: Read each completed sentence. Does it make
sense? Does the word you chose sound right with the
rest of the sentence?

Determining meaning from context: Using context after a blank

Follow the directions, and finish the picture.

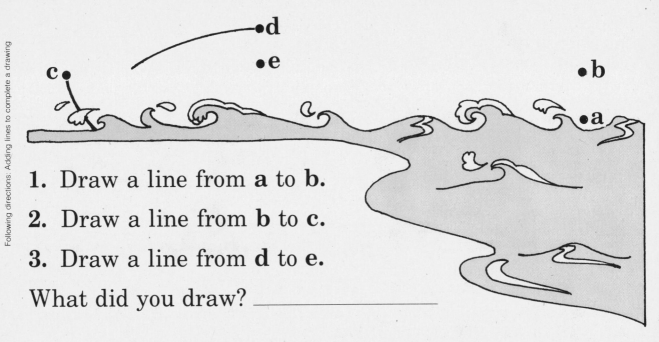

1. Draw a line from **a** to **b**.

2. Draw a line from **b** to **c**.

3. Draw a line from **d** to **e**.

What did you draw? _____

Follow the directions. Draw on the picture only what each direction tells you to draw.

1. Draw a long tail on the turtle. ☐

2. Draw a round hat on the turtle. ☐

3. Draw a feather coming out of the turtle's hat. ☐

4. Draw a beard on the turtle. ☐

CHECK: Read each direction again. Then look at your picture. Did you do what the direction told you to do?

Following directions: Adding lines to complete a drawing

Following directions: Completing a drawing

29

Mark the sentence that goes with the picture.

_____ Bob is giving a flower to Susie.

_____ Susie is giving a flower to a dog.

_____ Susie is giving a flower to Bob.

Circle the picture that goes with the sentence.

The mouse sat on the cheese.

30

Circle the word that makes the sentence silly. The first one is done for you.

1. You can throw stones, cans, (trees) and balls. ☐

2. You can see smoke, air, clouds, and fire. ☐

3. You can smell moonlight, flowers, onions, and soap. ☐

4. You can hear records, radios, pictures, and bands. ☐

CHECK: Read each sentence without the word you circled. It should make sense.

Mark the silly sentence. Then circle the word that makes it silly.

1. ____ Tom shut the door behind him.
   ____ Tom shut the table behind him. ☐

2. ____ The dog chased the ball across the park.
   ____ The stick chased the ball across the park. ☐

CHECK: Read each sentence you did not mark. It should make sense.

Mark the best answer to each question.

1. Which is shiniest? □

    _____ a new penny

    _____ a rotten orange

    _____ an old shoe

2. Which is deepest? □

    _____ a puddle

    _____ the sea

    _____ a stream

3. Which is most sour? □

    _____ a lemon

    _____ a peach

    _____ a cake

4. Which is wettest? □

    _____ a book

    _____ a towel

    _____ a pond

5. Which is highest? □

    _____ an ant hill

    _____ a mountain

    _____ a house

6. Which is roundest? □

    _____ an egg

    _____ an orange

    _____ a banana

7. Which is most gentle? □

    _____ a lion

    _____ a gorilla

    _____ a kitten

Semantic ordering: Answering superlative questions

CHECK: Read each question and the answers again. Did you think about all three things before you marked the best answer?

Read each sentence. Then follow the directions to answer a question about the sentence. Print your answer in the blank.

1. **The jumping beans were small and yellow.**
   Print <u>one</u> <u>word</u> from the sentence.

   What size were the beans? _____ ☐

2. **Pedro grew carrots in his garden and parsley in his windowbox.**
   Print <u>one</u> <u>word</u> from the sentence.

   What did Pedro grow in his garden? _____ ☐

3. **Jan likes to drink cold milk and eat meat pie.**
   Print <u>one</u> <u>word</u> from the sentence.

   What kind of milk does Jan like to drink? _____ ☐

4. **Barb goes swimming on Saturday, never on Sunday.**
   Print <u>two</u> <u>words</u> from the sentence.

   When does Barb go swimming? _____ ☐

<u>CHECK</u>: Read each question and the word or words you printed. Do the words make a good answer to the question?

Mark the sentence that goes with the picture.

_____ Louie likes to bake chicken every Wednesday.

_____ Louie likes to buy bread from the stove.

_____ Louie likes to bake bread every Saturday.

Circle the picture that goes with the sentence.

April smiled at the very large bird.

Read each sentence printed in dark letters. Then mark the other sentence that means about the same thing. The first one is done for you.

1. **The small fish swam away.** □
   This sentence means about the same as:

   _____ The silly fish swam away.

   _✓_ The little fish swam away.

2. **Lu Ping rushed to the store.** □
   This sentence means about the same as:

   _____ Lu Ping hurried to the store.

   _____ Lu Ping walked to the store.

3. **Two large dogs slept on the lawn.** □
   This sentence means about the same as:

   _____ Two big dogs slept on the lawn.

   _____ Two small dogs slept on the lawn.

4. **Toss the ball to me.** □
   This sentence means about the same as:

   _____ Throw the ball to me.

   _____ Bring the ball to me.

CHECK: Read each dark sentence and the meaning you marked for it. Do they tell you the same thing?

Paraphrase: Identifying paraphrase sentences

Mark the silly sentence. Then circle the word that makes it silly.

1. ____ We write with pencils or pens. ☐

   ____ We write with pens or carrots.

2. ____ The fire was very cold. ☐

   ____ The snow was very cold.

CHECK: Read each sentence you did <u>not</u> mark. It should make sense.

Circle the word that makes the sentence silly.

1. Fish, meat, forks, and vegetables can all be cooked. ☐

2. Fathers, aunts, grandfathers, and uncles are all men. ☐

3. Saws, dogs, cats, and children can all be fed. ☐

4. Cars, apples, bananas, and lemons grow on trees. ☐

CHECK: Read each sentence without the word you circled. It should make sense.

Underline the best word to complete each sentence. Then print that word in the blank.

1. _____ can soak up more water

   Spills   Sponges   Sparks

   than wood. ☐

2. _____ fell on our city all day. ☐

   Rocks   Rain   Roads

3. Bows can be tied in _____. ☐

   sidewalks   hair   arrows

4. Nell put peanut butter on her _____. ☐

   bread   bed   bead

5. _____ sang in the tree. ☐

   Clouds   Birds   Pillows

6. The wind blew leaves onto the _____. ☐

   trees   road   moon

7. The pretty girl rode a _____. ☐

   letter   bike   cake

CHECK: Read each completed sentence. Does it make sense? Does the word you chose sound right with the rest of the sentence?

Read each sentence printed in dark letters. Then mark the other sentence that means about the same thing. The first one is done for you.

1. **The yellow toad hid in the bag.** ☐
   This sentence means about the same as:

   _____ The yellow toad hid in the box.

   _✓_ The yellow toad hid in the sack.

2. **Martha gave Herb a present.** ☐
   This sentence means about the same as:

   _____ Martha gave Herb a party.

   _____ Martha gave Herb a gift.

3. **The small rabbit jumped up and down.** ☐
   This sentence means about the same as:

   _____ The small rabbit leaped up and down.

   _____ The small rabbit ran up and down.

4. **The chicken stood on the unhappy goat.** ☐
   This sentence means about the same as:

   _____ The chicken stood on the sick goat.

   _____ The chicken stood on the sad goat.

CHECK: Read each dark sentence and the meaning you marked for it. Do they tell you the same thing?

Follow the directions, and finish the picture.

1. Draw a line from **a** to **b**.
2. Draw a line from **c** to **d**.
3. Draw a line from **e** to **f**.

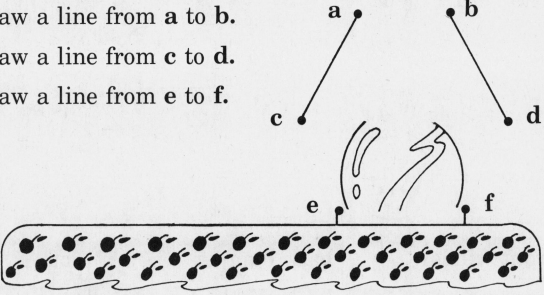

What did you draw? _____

Follow the directions, and finish the picture.

1. Draw a line from **a** to **b**.
2. Draw a line from **c** to **d**.
3. Draw a line from **d** to **e**.
4. Draw a line from **f** to **g**.

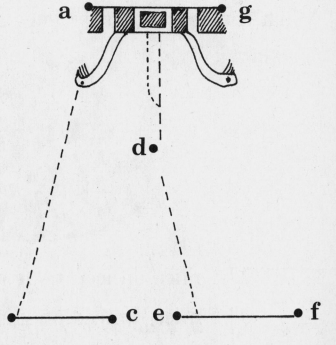

What did you draw? _____

Underline the things you need to draw to finish this car. Then draw them.

front window	back bumper	a roof
side window	back window	a body
front light	front wheel	doors
front bumper	back wheel	a wing

Mark the sentence that goes with the picture.

_____ The mice danced near the hat.

_____ The mice danced on the hat.

_____ The mice danced with the hat.

Mark the best answer to each question.

1. Which is slowest? ☐
   ____ a snail
   ____ a kitten
   ____ a horse

2. Which is strongest? ☐
   ____ a fox
   ____ an elephant
   ____ a rabbit

3. Which is longest? ☐
   ____ a river
   ____ a snake
   ____ a train

4. Which is softest? ☐
   ____ a rock
   ____ a shirt
   ____ a stick

5. Which eats most? ☐
   ____ a goldfish
   ____ a rock
   ____ a person

6. Which is heaviest? ☐
   ____ a goat
   ____ a balloon
   ____ a whale

7. Which costs most? ☐
   ____ shoes
   ____ gum
   ____ a ship

8. Which is smallest? ☐
   ____ a bug
   ____ a car
   ____ a lake

CHECK: Read each question and the answers again.
Did you think about all three things before you marked
the best answer?

Underline the best word to complete each sentence.
Then print that word in the blank.

1. Hamburgers, dimes, and pennies are all

    _____. ☐

     food   money   round

2. Girls, boys, and babies are all

    _____. ☐

     people   grown-ups   boys

3. Cars, trains, and bicycles all have

    _____. ☐

     tracks   wheels   gas

4. Kittens, puppies, chicks, and bear cubs are all

    _____. ☐

     large animals   baby animals   wild animals

5. Fish, dogs, whales, and ducks can all

    _____. ☐

     swim   bark   fly

CHECK: Read each completed sentence. Does the word
you chose fit each thing in the sentence? Think about
each one.

Synthesis: Completing classification sentences

Read each sentence, and look at each picture. Circle the word in each sentence that is wrong. Then print a better word above it. The first one is done for you.

1. The mouse hit the
spoon
bell with a (fork.) ☐

2. Frank the Frog swam over the pig. ☐

CHECK: Read each sentence the new way. Does it go with the picture?

Mark the silly sentence. Then circle the word that makes it silly.

1. ____ The sheep wanted to rest for a while.

____ The shoe wanted to rest for a while. ☐

2. ____ The duck couldn't paint under water.

____ The duck couldn't quack under water. ☐

CHECK: Read each sentence you did <u>not</u> mark. It should make sense.

Underline the best word to complete each sentence. Then print that word in the blank.

1. Hair, paper, lawns, and string are all things

   that we can _____. □

   wash   cut   paint

2. Coins, comic books, stamps, and baseball cards are all

   things that we can _____. □

   eat   spend   save

CHECK: Read each completed sentence. Does the word you chose fit each thing in the sentence? Think about each one.

———————————————————

Read each question. Then print a word in the blank to complete the answer.

1. Which is it—a balloon, a frog, or a banana?

   You peel it, so it must be a _____. □

2. Which is it—a fish, a person, or a fox?

   It has four feet, so it must be a _____. □

CHECK: Read each completed sentence.
Does it make sense?

Synthesis: Completing classification sentences

Synthesis: Solving structured riddles

Read the question. Then mark the sentence that answers the question.

Why do shoes squeak? ☐

_____ Shoes squeak because their parts rub together.

_____ Some shoes squeak more loudly than others.

CHECK: Read the question and the sentence you marked. Does the sentence really answer the question?

━━━━━━━━━━━━━━━━━━━━━━━━━━━━━━━━━━━━

Read each sentence. Then follow the directions to answer a question about the sentence. Print your answer in the blank.

1. **Bess beat Bob in a game of checkers yesterday.**
   Print one word from the sentence.

   When did Bob and Bess play checkers?

   _____ ☐

2. **Susan wore mittens on her feet and boots on her hands.**
   Print one word from the sentence.

   What did Susan wear on her feet? _____ ☐

CHECK: Read each question and the word you printed. Does the word make a good answer to the question?

Circle the picture that goes with the sentence.

The elephant is beside the truck.

Mark the sentence that goes with the picture.

_____ The carrot chased the bug.

_____ The bat chased the carrot.

_____ The bug chased the carrot.

Using imagery: Selecting a picture to illustrate a sentence

Using imagery: Selecting a sentence to describe a picture

Mark the best answer to each question.

1. Which <u>looks</u> most like a ball? ☐

_____ a book   _____ an apple   _____ a pear

2. Which <u>feels</u> most like glass? ☐

_____ ice   _____ grass   _____ sand

3. Which <u>looks</u> most like a cup? ☐

_____ a bowl   _____ a spoon   _____ a bridge

_____

Mark the best answer to each question.

1. Which is coldest? ☐

_____ summer   _____ milk   _____ ice cream

2. Which is flattest? ☐

_____ a paper   _____ a hamburger   _____ a garden

3. Which is roundest? ☐

_____ a bat   _____ a ball   _____ a glove

<u>CHECK</u>: Read each question and the answers again. Did you think about all three things before you marked the best answer?

Follow the directions. Draw on the picture only what each direction tells you to draw.

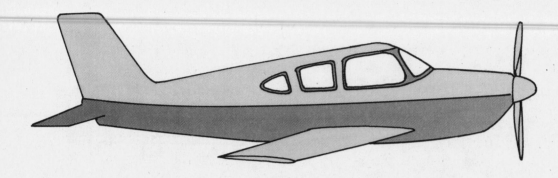

1. Draw a circle on the tail of the airplane. ☐

2. Draw an X inside the circle you just drew. ☐

3. Draw a pilot's head inside the cockpit (the place where the pilot sits). ☐

4. Draw a cloud above the airplane. ☐

CHECK: Read each direction again. Then look at your picture. Did you do what the direction told you to do?

Following directions: Completing a drawing

_____

Follow the directions, and finish the picture.

1. Draw a line from **a** to **b**.

2. Draw a line from **b** to **c**.

3. Draw a line from **c** to **d**.

4. Draw a line from **d** to **e**.

What did you draw? _____

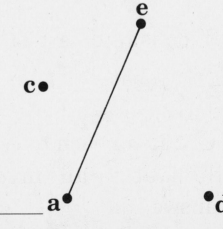

Following directions: Adding lines to complete a drawing

Read each sentence, and look at each picture. Circle the word in each sentence that is wrong. Then print a better word above it.

1. A happy snake is out in the rain. ☐

2. Helen Hen is hanging up her raincoat. ☐

CHECK: Read each sentence the new way. Does it go with the picture?

Circle the word that makes the sentence silly.

1. You can ride in boats, trains, tools, and cars. ☐

2. You can buy books, boots, days, and pots. ☐

3. You can wash dishes, towns, shirts, and faces. ☐

CHECK: Read each sentence without the word you circled. It should make sense.

Underline the best word to complete each sentence. Then print that word in the blank.

1. Windows, screens, and air are all easy to

   _____ through. ☐

   see   shut   break

2. Horns, crows, and fire engines are all

   _____. ☐

   noisy   black   fast

CHECK: Read each completed sentence. Does the word you chose fit each thing in the sentence? Think about each one.

Read each question. Then print a word in the blank to complete the answer.

1. Which is it—a lake, a tree, or a needle?

   You climb it, so it must be a _____. ☐

2. Which is it—a horn, a flag, or a hat?

   You blow it, so it must be a _____. ☐

CHECK: Read each completed sentence. Does it make sense?

Read each question. Then mark the sentence that answers the question.

1. What is a cup? ☐

    ____ A cup is a kind of dish that we drink from.

    ____ A cup has a handle to hang on to.

2. Why do people use soap? ☐

    ____ Many people use soap every day.

    ____ People use soap to keep themselves clean.

CHECK: Read each question and the sentence you marked. Does the sentence really answer the question?

Read the sentence. Then follow the directions to answer a question about the sentence. Print your answer in the blank.

Bram always sang in the bathtub on Saturday.
Print three words from the sentence.

Where did Bram always sing?

_____ ☐

CHECK: Read the question and the words you printed. Do the words make a good answer to the question?

Read each sentence printed in dark letters. Then mark the other sentence that means about the same thing.

1. **Cora put the books in the chest.** □
   This sentence means about the same as:

   _____ Cora put the books in the closet.

   _____ Cora put the books in the trunk.

2. **Kerry told me a funny story.** □
   This sentence means about the same as:

   _____ Kerry told me a joke.

   _____ Kerry told me a lie.

3. **Pick the best book.** □
   This sentence means about the same as:

   _____ Choose the best book.

   _____ Read the best book.

4. **They fell into very cold water.** □
   This sentence means about the same as:

   _____ They fell into deep water.

   _____ They fell into icy water.

CHECK: Read each dark sentence and the meaning you marked for it. Do they tell you the same thing?

Circle the word in each sentence that is wrong.
Then print a better word above it.

1. Mr. Jones drove up in his new corn. ☐

2. You use a pencil and a boat to write. ☐

CHECK: Read each sentence the new way. Does it
make sense?

Read each sentence, and look at each picture. Circle the
word in each sentence that is wrong. Then print a better
word above it.

1. A small fish walks

in its bowl. ☐

2. The worm sat on the

chair and waved. ☐

CHECK: Read each sentence the new way. Does it go
with the picture?

53

Underline the best word to complete each sentence. Then print that word in the blank.

1. Your foot has five _____. ☐

                shoes   fingers   toes

2. _____ can get in your eyes. ☐

   Ears   Goldfish   Dust

3. _____ have legs, but they

   People   Tigers   Tables

never walk. ☐

4. _____ live in the oceans of

   Sharks   Sheep   Deer

the world. ☐

5. Birds can fly because they have

_____. ☐

   legs   wings   beaks

CHECK: Read each completed sentence. Does it make sense? Does the word you chose sound right with the rest of the sentence?

Determining meaning from context: Using context before or after a blank

1. Look at the picture. Then read the story, and underline the words that tell about two things the artist forgot to draw. Do not underline anything else.

Kelly was ready for the pitch. She was wearing her lucky cap and her black running shoes. She was holding her baseball bat like a pro.

2. Now add to the picture the things you underlined.

Circle the word in each sentence that is wrong. Then print a better word above it.

1. My warm coat is made of wood. ☐

2. The snake hurt its foot and could not run. ☐

CHECK: Read each sentence the new way. Does it make sense?

Read the sentence. Then follow the directions to answer a question about the sentence. Print your answer in the blank.

Dixie plays the trumpet, and Barry plays the big drum.

Print <u>three</u> <u>words</u> from the sentence.

What does Barry play? _____ ☐

<u>CHECK</u>: Read the question and the words you printed. Do the words make a good answer to the question?

Read each question. Then mark the sentence that answers the question.

1. Where do some fish live? ☐

    _____ Some fish live in icy cold rivers and lakes.

    _____ Some fish live for a very long time.

2. How are crocodiles and bears the same? ☐

    _____ Crocodiles and bears both like to eat fish.

    _____ Crocodiles cannot walk on two feet like a bear.

<u>CHECK</u>: Read each question and the sentence you marked. Does the sentence really answer the question?

Mark the best answer to each question.

1. Which <u>feels</u> most like worms? ☐

   ____ beans

   ____ sheets

   ____ spaghetti

2. Which <u>smells</u> most like perfume? ☐

   ____ a skunk

   ____ smoke

   ____ a flower

3. Which <u>looks</u> most like salt? ☐

   ____ pepper

   ____ sand

   ____ rain

4. Which <u>acts</u> most like a horse? ☐

   ____ a cat

   ____ a crow

   ____ a zebra

5. Which <u>tastes</u> most like soup? ☐

   ____ stew

   ____ bread

   ____ an apple

6. Which <u>looks</u> most like a wolf? ☐

   ____ a dog

   ____ a deer

   ____ a bear

<u>CHECK:</u> Read each question and the answers again. Did you think about all three things before you marked the best answer?

1. Look at the picture. Then read the story, and underline the words that tell about two things the artist forgot to draw. Do not underline anything else.

> Nick wanted both toys, but he had to choose.
> One toy was a large ball with stripes. The other
> was a wagon with a long handle.

2. Now add to the picture the things you underlined.

Circle the word in each sentence that is wrong. Then print a better word above it.

1. The girls washed the noses off their faces. □

2. Sean pulled a loose ear out of his mouth. □

CHECK: Read each sentence the new way. Does it make sense?

Circle the picture that goes with the sentence.

Beth carried a broom on her nose.

Underline the things you need to draw to finish this airplane. Then draw them.

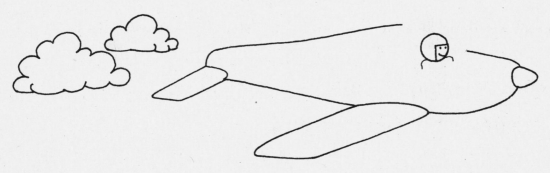

a sun   a propeller   a cockpit (the place
                                where the pilot sits)
one wing   birds

a body   a tail   windows

a cloud   a mountain   legs

Underline the best word to complete each sentence. Then print that word in the blank.

1. Cows, kites, planes, and alligators can all have

   _____. ☐

   babies   wings   tails

2. Glasses, sticks, windows, and icicles can all

   _____. ☐

   break   grow   melt

CHECK: Read each completed sentence. Does the word you chose fit each thing in the sentence? Think about each one.

Read each question. Then print a word in the blank to complete the answer.

1. Which is it—soap, paint, or coal?

   You wash with it, so it must be _____. ☐

2. Which is it—a fork, a needle, or a pencil?

   You write with it, so it must be a _____. ☐

CHECK: Read each completed sentence. Does it make sense?

Circle the word in each sentence that is wrong.
Then print a better word above it.

1. Lee wore a bus around his wrist. ☐

2. Anne liked to drink hills when she was thirsty. ☐

CHECK: Read each sentence the new way. Does it
make sense?

Read each sentence, and look at each picture. Circle the
word in each sentence that is wrong. Then print a better
word above it.

1. The crow flew over

the house at night. ☐

2. Two children are

eating the huge beet. ☐

CHECK: Read each sentence the new way. Does it go
with the picture?

1. First read this story.

Mammoths lived long, long ago. They looked like huge, shaggy elephants. No mammoths are alive now.

2. Now underline the sentence or the words in the story that answer each question below. Then copy the words you underlined onto the blanks.

What did mammoths look like? ☐

_____

How many mammoths are alive now? ☐

_____

CHECK: Read each question and the answer you copied. Does it really answer the question?

Read the sentence. Then follow the directions to answer a question about the sentence.

Nina went to a movie, but Linda went to the zoo.
Print <u>three</u> <u>words</u> from the sentence.

Where did Nina go? _____ ☐

CHECK: Read the question and the words you printed. Do the words make a good answer to the question?

Locating answers to questions: Answering factual "wh" questions by quoting the text

Locating answers to questions: Isolating sentence parts as answers

Read each sentence printed in dark letters. Then mark the other sentence that means about the same thing.

1. **Some birds have very pretty feathers.** □
   This sentence means about the same as:

   _____ Some birds have dull feathers.

   _____ Some birds have beautiful feathers.

2. **The weather was very warm in July.** □
   This sentence means about the same as:

   _____ The weather was cloudy in July.

   _____ The weather was hot in July.

3. **My frog hopped over the log.** □
   This sentence means about the same as:

   _____ My frog jumped over the log.

   _____ My frog fell over the log.

4. **Kim will speak to the farmer.** □
   This sentence means about the same as:

   _____ Kim will sing to the farmer.

   _____ Kim will talk to the farmer.

CHECK: Read each dark sentence and the meaning you marked for it. Do they tell you the same thing?

1. First read this story.

Robert Peary was an American. He led the first group that went to the North Pole. A man from Norway named Roald Amundsen was the first person at the South Pole.

2. Now underline the sentence or the words in the story that answer each question below. Then copy the words you underlined onto the blanks.

What did Robert Peary do? ☐

_____

_____

Who was the first person to reach the South Pole? ☐

_____

_____

CHECK: Read each question and the answer you copied. Does it really answer the question?

Juan put three frogs in Tim's pocket.

Print <u>three</u> <u>words</u> from the sentence.

Where did Juan put the three frogs?

_____ ☐

64

Follow the directions, and finish the picture.

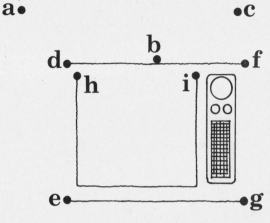

1. Draw a line from **a** to **b**.

2. Draw a line from **b** to **c**.

3. Draw a line from **d** to **e**.

4. Draw a line from **f** to **g**.

5. Draw a line from **h** to **i**.

What did you draw? _____

Follow the directions. Draw on the picture only what each direction tells you to draw.

1. Draw two doors on the side of the car. ☐

2. Draw a handle for each door. ☐

3. Draw a girl's face in the back window. ☐

4. Draw a light at the front of the car. ☐

CHECK: Read each direction again. Then look at your picture. Did you do what the direction told you to do?

1. Tess dropped the bowl because she was upset.

Print <u>four</u> <u>words</u> from the sentence.

Why did Tess drop the bowl?

_____ □

2. Yesterday June tried to eat her soup with a fork.

Print <u>three</u> <u>words</u> from the sentence.

How did June try to eat soup? _____ □

<u>CHECK</u>: Read each question and the words you printed. Do the words make a good answer to the question?

Mark the sentence that answers each question.

1. How do frogs move? □

_____ Frogs hop and swim.

_____ Frogs live in ponds and swamps.

2. Why do wolves howl? □

_____ Wolves howl at night.

_____ Wolves howl to call each other.

<u>CHECK</u>: Read each question and the sentence you marked. Does the sentence really answer the question?

1. Look at the picture. Then read the story, and underline the words that tell about two things the artist forgot to draw. Do not underline anything else.

Ali and Alia are riding on a flying carpet.

Ali is hanging onto his hat. Alia is hanging on to a basket. That way nothing will be lost.

2. Now add to the picture the things you underlined.

Circle the word in each sentence that is wrong. Then print a better word above it.

1. I like to feed pencils to the squirrels. ☐

2. The sun blew all the petals off the roses. ☐

<u>CHECK</u>: Read each sentence the new way. Does it make sense?

Underline the word that makes each sentence go with the picture. Then print that word in the blank.

1. You can see a bee

_____

over   under   on

the grapes. ☐

2. A bear is trying to hide

_____

above   over   behind

the tall grass. ☐

CHECK: Read each completed sentence. Does it go with the picture?

Mark the sentence that goes with the picture.

_____ The fox wearing the cap followed the sheep.

_____ The sheep wearing the cap followed the dog.

_____ The dog wearing the cap followed the sheep.

68

1. First read this story.

> Something strange lives on the other side of the world. It is a worm that grows to be twice as long as a bed! It looks like a huge American earthworm. That is why it is called the giant earthworm.

2. Now underline the sentence or the words in the story that answer each question below. Then copy the words you underlined onto the blanks.

Where does the giant earthworm live? □

_____

_____

How big is the giant earthworm? □

_____

_____

CHECK: Read each question and the answer you copied. Does it really answer the question?

Underline the best word to complete each sentence. Then print that word in the blank.

1. _____ are filled with words

   Talks   Books   Beds

   and pictures. ☐

2. The horses lived in a big red _____. ☐

   barn   berry   bus

3. _____ come to you when

   Rocks   Dreams   Friends

   you sleep. ☐

4. You can never catch a _____. ☐

   shadow   baseball   cold

5. Ernie packed all his clothes in a

   _____. ☐

   cup   suitcase   cloud

CHECK: Read each completed sentence. Does it make sense? Does the word you chose sound right with the rest of the sentence?

Determining meaning from context: Using context before or after a blank

Underline the best word to complete each sentence.
Then print that word in the blank.

1. Eagles, dogs, cats, and lizards are all animals with

   _____. ☐

   feathers   tails   fur

2. Soft, hard, smooth, and rough all tell how things

   _____. ☐

   smell   taste   feel

CHECK: Read each completed sentence. Does the word
you chose fit each thing in the sentence? Think about
each one.

Read each question. Then print a word in the blank to
complete the answer.

1. Which is it—a worm, a wolf, or a chicken?

   It has sharp teeth, so it must be a _____. ☐

2. Which is it—morning, noon, or night?

   It is dark, so it must be _____. ☐

CHECK: Read each completed sentence. Does it
make sense?

1. First read this story.

> The egg-eating snake eats eggs. It eats nothing but eggs. The egg-eating snake will eat eggs of any shape or size. It never eats the eggshells.

2. Now underline the sentence or the words in the story that answer each question below. Then copy the words you underlined onto the blanks.

What eggs will the egg-eating snake eat? □

_____

_____

What is it that the egg-eating snake never eats? □

_____

_____

CHECK: Read each question and the answer you copied. Does it really answer the question?

Lian hung the picture on the wall yesterday.
Print three words from the sentence.

Where did Lian hang the picture?

_____ □

Locating answers to questions: Answering factual "wh" questions by quoting the text

Locating answers to questions: Isolating sentence parts as answers

Underline the word that makes the sentence go with the picture. Then print that word in the blank.

The sly fox is _____ the porch. □

         above   beside   behind

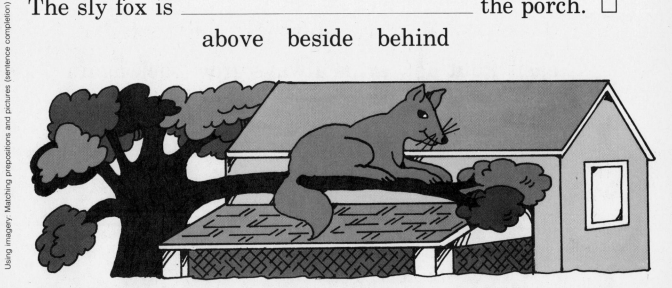

CHECK: Read the completed sentence. Does it go with the picture?

Circle the picture that goes with the sentence.

The rabbit jumps over the television set.

1. First read this story.

> Most stars are in the sky, but brittle stars are found in the sea. Brittle stars are sea animals that are shaped like stars. Their arms fall off easily, but new arms always grow back again.

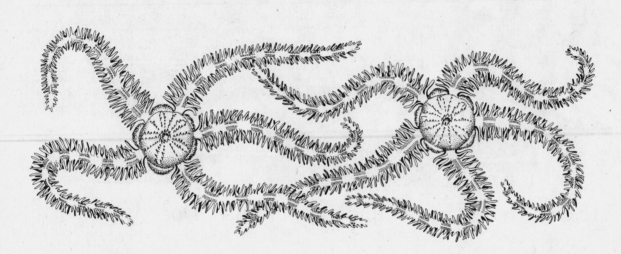

2. Now underline the sentence or the words in the story that answer each question below. Then copy the words you underlined onto the blanks.

Where are brittle stars found? ☐

_____

_____

What happens when a brittle star's arms fall off? ☐

_____

_____

CHECK: Read each question and the answer you copied. Does it really answer the question?

Locating answers to questions: Answering factual "wh" questions by quoting the text

Underline the word that makes each sentence go with the picture. Then print that word in the blank.

1. The fat frog is _____ the bird's

under   beside   inside

nest. ☐

2. The pencil is trying to hide

_____ the thread. ☐

beside   behind   under

3. Mr. Chan's foot is caught

_____ the big jam jar. ☐

inside   over   under

<u>CHECK:</u> Read each completed sentence. Does it go with the picture?

Using imagery: Matching prepositions and pictures (sentence completion)

Read each pair of sentences. Then complete the second sentence to tell why the first sentence is silly.

1. Billy ate a sandwich and a balloon.

   Billy would not eat a _____. ☐

2. Some snakes run very fast in the grass.

   Snakes cannot _____. ☐

CHECK: Read each sentence you completed. Is it true? Does it tell what's wrong with the first sentence of the pair?

1. Look at the picture. Then read the story, and underline the words that tell about two things the artist forgot to draw. Do not underline anything else.

   We saw two special animals at the circus. One was a monkey with its tail around a swing. The other was a seal balancing a ball on its nose.

2. Now add to the picture the things you underlined.

Read the story. Then answer each question **yes** or **no**. Finally, follow the directions to show that your answer is right.

> Long ago people did not live in houses. They lived in caves. Sometimes they painted pictures of animals on their cave walls. Some of these pictures can still be seen today.

1. Did people always live in houses? _____

Copy the sentence from the story that tells you. ☐

_____

_____

2. Did these people paint pictures of animals? _____

Copy the sentence from the story that tells you. ☐

_____

_____

<u>CHECK</u>: Read each sentence you copied. Does it show that your answer is right?

_____

The bugs in the jar were eating coffee from Brazil.
Print <u>three</u> <u>words</u> from the sentence.

Where were the bugs? _____ ☐

Locating answers to questions: Supporting yes-no answers by quoting the text

Locating answers to questions: Isolating sentence parts as answers

Mark the best answer to each question.

1. Which <u>feels</u> most like the sun? ☐

   ____ the sea

   ____ a fire

   ____ a snake

2. Which <u>sounds</u> most like a car? ☐

   ____ a bed

   ____ a truck

   ____ music

3. Which <u>flies</u> most like a bird? ☐

   ____ a balloon

   ____ a bee

   ____ a leaf

4. Which <u>looks</u> most like a baseball? ☐

   ____ a football

   ____ a duck

   ____ a beach ball

5. Which <u>acts</u> most like a person? ☐

   ____ a fly

   ____ a monkey

   ____ a shark

6. Which <u>feels</u> most like sandpaper? ☐

   ____ a sidewalk

   ____ a mirror

   ____ a puddle

CHECK: Read each question and the answers again. Did you think about all three things before you marked the best answer?

Semantic ordering: Answering questions of similarity

Read the story. Then answer each question **yes** or **no**. Finally, follow the directions to show that your answer is right.

Apes do not have tails as monkeys do. That is how you tell them apart. The biggest ape of all is the gorilla. Even though gorillas may seem mean, they make fine parents. They are very gentle with their young.

1. Do apes have tails? _____

Copy the sentence from the story that tells you. ☐

_____

_____

2. Is a gorilla an ape? _____

Copy the sentence from the story that tells you. ☐

_____

_____

CHECK: Read each sentence you copied. Does it show that your answer is right?

Follow the directions, and finish the picture.

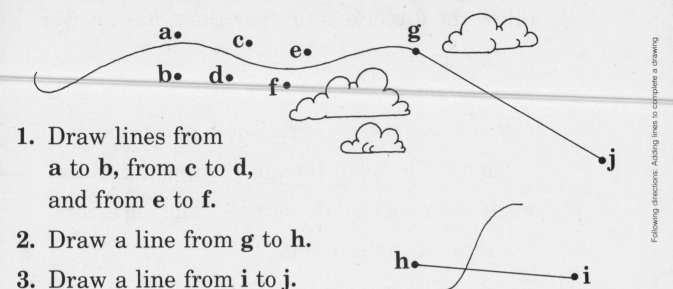

1. Draw lines from
   a to **b**, from **c** to **d**,
   and from **e** to **f**.

2. Draw a line from **g** to **h**.

3. Draw a line from **i** to **j**.

What did you draw? _____

Follow the directions.
Draw on the picture only what
each direction tells you to draw.

1. Draw a basketball in
   the player's hand. ☐

2. Draw two ears on the
   player's head. ☐

3. Draw a T-shirt on the
   player. ☐

4. Draw a smile on his face. ☐

CHECK: Read each direction again. Then look at your
picture. Did you do what the direction told you to do?

Read each pair of sentences. Then complete the second sentence to tell why the first sentence is silly.

1. Harry says that his chicken lays eggs and barks.

   A chicken cannot _____. ☐

2. Judi likes the way catsup makes her food look blue.

   Catsup isn't _____. ☐

CHECK: Read each sentence you completed. Is it true? Does it tell what's wrong with the first sentence of the pair?

Read each sentence, and look at each picture. Circle the word in each sentence that is wrong. Then print a better word above it.

1. The big duck is carrying a suitcase. ☐

2. The cowboy is sitting on a horse. ☐

CHECK: Read each sentence the new way. Does it go with the picture?

Underline the best word or words to complete each sentence. Then print the word or words in the blank.

1. Every house has a _____ to let people
   roof   radio   door
   get in and out. ☐

2. A chicken has a _____ on its face. ☐
   wing   beak   neck

3. Delfun brushed his _____ with a new
   hair   dog   teeth
   kind of toothpaste. ☐

4. Cindy kept her _____ safely in
   pony   money   bicycle
   her pocket. ☐

5. Manny licked a _____
   stone   stamp   crayon
   and put it on a letter. ☐

CHECK: Read each completed sentence. Does it make sense? Does the word or words you chose sound right with the rest of the sentence?

Determining meaning from context: Using context *around* a blank

1. First read this story.

> The Bombay duck is not even a bird. It is really a small fish with long, sharp teeth. People in India catch Bombay ducks in nets. Then they dry, salt, and eat the little fish.

2. Now underline the sentence or the words in the story that answer each question below. Then copy the words you underlined onto the blanks.

What is the Bombay duck? ☐

_____

_____

What do people do with the Bombay duck? ☐

_____

CHECK: Read each question and the answer you copied. Does it really answer the question?

Mark the sentence that answers the question.

How are elephants and horses the same? ☐

_____ Horses are smaller than elephants.

_____ Horses and elephants can both sleep standing up.

Underline the word that makes the sentence go with the picture. Then print that word in the blank.

The umbrella is

_____

inside   over   behind

the rat's head. □

<u>CHECK</u>: Read the completed sentence. Does it go with the picture?

Circle the picture that goes with the sentence.

The rat wore the cat's rubber boots.

Read each sentence printed in dark letters. Then mark the other sentence that means about the same thing.

1. **Place the cup on the table.** ☐
   This sentence means about the same as:

   _____ Throw the cup on the table.

   _____ Put the cup on the table.

2. **Everyone looked at the cartoons.** ☐
   This sentence means about the same as:

   _____ Everyone watched the cartoons.

   _____ Everyone laughed at the cartoons.

3. **A lot of people were waiting in line.** ☐
   This sentence means about the same as:

   _____ Many people were waiting in line.

   _____ A few people were waiting in line.

4. **Meg was not ever afraid.** ☐
   This sentence means about the same as:

   _____ Meg was never frightened.

   _____ Meg was often afraid.

CHECK: Read each dark sentence and the meaning you marked for it. Do they tell you the same thing?

Read the story. Then answer each question **yes** or **no**. Finally, follow the directions to show that your answer is right.

The climbing perch is a fish that lives in rivers and ponds. It can't really climb. It <u>can</u> travel on land and go from pond to pond. So some places you must be careful not to step on the fish.

1. Can the climbing perch climb? _____
   Copy the sentence from the story that tells you. ☐

   _____

2. Can the climbing perch travel on land? _____
   Copy the sentence from the story that tells you. ☐

   _____

   _____

CHECK: Read each sentence you copied. Does it show that your answer is right?

Pat found the note that Jim left in her shoe.
Print <u>one</u> <u>word</u> from the sentence.

Who put the note in the shoe? _____ ☐

Locating answers to questions: Supporting yes-no answers by quoting the text

Locating answers to questions: Isolating sentence parts as answers

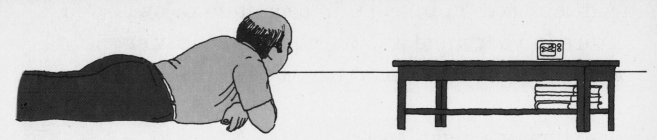

1. Look at the picture. Then read the story, and underline the words that tell about <u>three</u> things the artist forgot to draw. Do not underline anything else.

Mr. Blister is lying on the floor in front of his big and little TV sets. He is watching two shows at once. A glass of milk and a bowl of popcorn are on the floor beside him.

2. Now add to the picture the things you underlined.

Read the pair of sentences. Then complete the second sentence to tell why the first sentence is silly.

Dora took a bite from the juicy black apple.

Apples are not _____. ☐

<u>CHECK</u>: Read the sentence you completed. Is it true? Does it tell what's wrong with the first sentence of the pair?

87

Read sentences **a, b,** and **c** in each item below. Get a picture in your mind as you read. Then answer the question. Print your answer in the blank.

1. **a.** Imagine a garden hose. ☐
   b. Give the hose two eyes and a tail. ☐
   c. Now make the hose move through the grass by itself. ☐

   What does it look like now? _____

2. **a.** Imagine a lion. ☐
   b. Take away the lion's mane. ☐
   c. Now give the lion stripes. ☐

   What does it look like now? _____

<u>CHECK</u>: Read sentences **a, b,** and **c** in each item again. Did you imagine <u>all</u> the changes?

Underline the word that makes the sentence go with the picture. Then print that word in the blank.

The ant is standing

_____

   under   on   behind

the goat's nose. ☐

Using imagery: Changing mental images

Using imagery: Matching prepositions and pictures (sentence completion)

Read each sentence, and look at each picture. Circle the word in each sentence that is wrong. Then print a better word above it.

1. Harvey had the word hero printed on his shirt. ☐

2. The snowman had rocks for eyes and a potato for a nose. ☐

CHECK: Read each sentence the new way. Does it go with the picture?

Read the pair of sentences. Then complete the second sentence to tell why the first sentence is silly.

The robin's fur kept it warm in winter.

Robins do not have _____. ☐

CHECK: Read the sentence you completed. Is it true? Does it tell what's wrong with the first sentence?

Read sentences **a, b,** and **c** below. Get a picture in your mind as you read. Then answer the question. Print your answer in the blank.

a. Imagine a piece of thread. ☐
b. Make it much thicker. ☐
c. Now make it much longer. ☐

What does it look like now? _____

CHECK: Read sentences **a, b,** and **c** again. Did you imagine all the changes?

Underline the things you need to draw to finish this bicycle. Then draw them.

a light   a chain   a window

a trunk   a fender   a seat

a wheel   a door   a foot pedal

a handlebar   a basket   a motor

Circle the word in each sentence that is wrong.
Then print a better word above it.

1. All cars have square wheels. □

2. We cooked the soup on the chair. □

CHECK: Read each sentence the new way. Does it make sense?

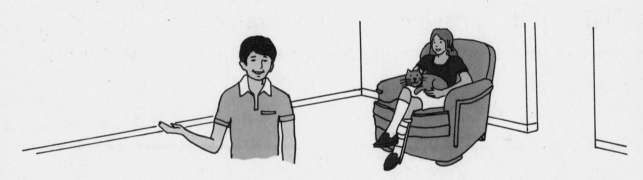

1. Look at the picture. Then read the story, and underline the words that tell about <u>three</u> things the artist forgot to draw. Do not underline anything else.

> Janet is watching Boris walk with a book on his head. He has a candle in his hand. Janet is sitting in a chair with her cat in her lap. Her book is on the floor. She is too busy watching Boris to read.

2. Now add to the picture the things you underlined.

Underline the best word to complete each sentence.
Then print that word in the blank.

1. Bowls, houses, pencils, and chairs can all be made of

   _____. ☐

       glass   lead   wood

2. Books, party hats, money, and bags can all be made

   of _____. ☐

       paper   metal   cloth

CHECK: Read each completed sentence. Does the word
you chose fit each thing in the sentence? Think about
each one.

Synthesis: Completing classification sentences

Read each question. Then print a word in the blank to
complete the answer.

1. Which is it—a desk, a radio, or a bed?

   It talks, so it must be a _____. ☐

2. Which is it—a hammer, a crayon, or a clock?

   You draw with it, so it must be a _____. ☐

Synthesis: Solving structured riddles

CHECK: Read each completed sentence.
Does it make sense?

Underline the word that makes the sentence go with the picture. Then print that word in the blank.

The tiny bug is

_____

on   between   over

the bricks. ☐

CHECK: Read the completed sentence. Does it go with the picture?

Read sentences **a, b,** and **c** below. Get a picture in your mind as you read. Then answer the question. Print your answer in the blank.

a. Imagine a handful of salt. ☐
b. Give the salt a golden color. ☐
c. Now take away the salty taste. ☐

What does it look like now? _____

CHECK: Read sentences **a, b,** and **c** again. Did you imagine all the changes?

1. First read this story.

> The little bamboo bat is the smallest bat in the world. It is about as long as your big toe. It has pads on its feet. These pads help it to walk on smooth things.

2. Now underline the sentence or the words in the story that answer each question below. Then copy the words you underlined onto the blanks.

How long is the little bamboo bat? ☐

_____

_____

What helps the little bamboo bat to walk on smooth things? ☐

_____

_____

Mark the sentence that answers the question.

What are clocks used for? ☐

_____ Clocks tell us what time it is.

_____ Clocks have round faces and two hands.

Read each sentence, and look at each picture. Circle the word in each sentence that is wrong. Then print a better word above it.

1. The giraffe's bowl is tipping over. ☐

2. Tatu's pants are much too large for her. ☐

CHECK: Read each sentence the new way. Does it go with the picture?

Read the pair of sentences. Then complete the second sentence to tell why the first sentence is silly.

Consuelo likes elephants because they have trunks, big ears, and wings.

Elephants do not have _____. ☐

CHECK: Read the sentence you completed. Is it true? Does it tell what's wrong with the first sentence of the pair?

Circle the picture that goes with the sentence.

The tiny whale swam in the cup.

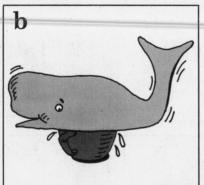

Read sentences **a, b,** and **c** in each item below. Get a picture in your mind as you read. Then answer the question. Print your answer in the blank.

1. **a.** Imagine a beautiful flower. ☐
   b. Make it ugly and bad smelling. ☐
   c. Make it grow where it is not wanted. ☐

   What is it now? _____

2. **a.** Imagine a bag of baseballs. ☐
   b. Make the baseballs very small and hard. ☐
   c. Now make the baseballs different colors. ☐

   What are they like now? _____

<u>CHECK:</u> Read sentences **a, b,** and **c** in each item again. Did you imagine <u>all</u> the changes?

Read the story. Then answer each question **yes** or **no.**
Finally, follow the directions to show that your answer
is right.

> There once was a bird called the dodo. It could
> not fly, and it could not run very well. It had no
> way to get away from people who caught it for
> food. No more dodos are alive today.

1. Could the dodo fly? _____

Copy the sentence from the story that tells you. ☐

_____

_____

2. Are dodos still alive today? _____

Copy the sentence from the story that tells you. ☐

_____

_____

Mark the sentence that answers the question.

What is a clown? ☐

_____ Some clowns like to eat pork chops.

_____ A clown is a person who makes us laugh.

Underline the best word to complete each sentence.
Then print that word in the blank.

1. I can see the _____ in the sky at
                      earth   sun   moon
   night. ☐

2. A jet plane is much _____ than
                          slower   faster   smaller
   a bird. ☐

3. You must open a _____ before you can
                    can   book   sign
   read it. ☐

4. The fat white _____ laid a small
                horse   hen   dog
   brown egg. ☐

5. The huge tree _____ from a tiny seed. ☐
              ate   ran   grew

6. The strings on my _____ are
                 guitar   trumpet   broom
   broken. ☐

CHECK: Read each completed sentence. Does it make sense? Does the word you chose sound right with the rest of the sentence?

1. Look at the picture. Then read the story, and underline the words that tell about <u>three</u> things the artist forgot to draw. Do not underline anything else.

The ox is pulling a wagon full of bags. The driver has long hair and wears big boots. Her pet wolf is on the seat beside her. A large tree is giving them some shade.

2. Now add to the picture the things you underlined.

Read the pair of sentences. Then complete the second sentence to tell why the first sentence is silly.

The whale likes to fly and swim in the ocean.

Whales do not _____. ☐

<u>CHECK</u>: Read the sentence you completed. Is it true? Does it tell what's wrong with the first sentence of the pair?

1. First read this story.

A flying fox is a very large bat. These bats eat fruit instead of insects. Farmers do not like these bats, because they eat the fruit the farmers grow.

2. Now underline the sentence or the words in the story that answer each question below. Then copy the words you underlined onto the blanks.

What is a flying fox? ☐

_____

_____

What kind of food does the flying fox eat? ☐

_____

_____

Mark the sentence that answers the question.

What is the blue whale? ☐

_____ The blue whale is about a hundred feet long.

_____ The blue whale is the world's biggest animal.

Locating answers to questions: Answering factual "wh" questions by quoting the text

Locating answers to questions: Recognizing answer sentences

Follow the directions. Draw on the picture only what each direction tells you to draw.

1. Draw a seat on the bicycle. □

2. Draw foot pedals on the bicycle. □

3. Draw spokes on the wheels. □

4. Draw a basket above the light on the bicycle's handlebars. □

CHECK: Read each direction again. Then look at your picture. Did you do what the direction told you to do?

Follow the directions, and finish the picture.

1. Draw a line from **a** to **b**.

2. Draw lines from **a** to **c** and from **b** to **f**.

3. Draw a line from **d** to **e**.

4. Draw a line from **g** to **h**.

5. Draw a line from **i** to **j**.

What did you draw? _____

Read each sentence printed in dark letters. Then mark the other sentence that means about the same thing.

1. **Herb buys cheap toys.** □
   This sentence means about the same as:

   _____ Herb buys toys that do not cost much.

   _____ Herb buys toys that cost a lot.

2. **The water was too deep for Stan.** □
   This sentence means about the same as:

   _____ The water was too thick for Stan.

   _____ The water was over Stan's head.

3. **I washed the dishes after dinner.** □
   This sentence means about the same as:

   _____ I washed the meat and potatoes after dinner.

   _____ I washed the plates and cups after dinner.

4. **The music was too loud for me.** □
   This sentence means about the same as:

   _____ The music hurt my ears.

   _____ The music made me laugh.

CHECK: Read each dark sentence and the meaning you marked for it. Do they tell you the same thing?

Paraphrase: Identifying paraphrase sentences

Read sentences **a, b,** and **c** below. Get a picture in your mind as you read. Then answer the question. Print your answer in the blank.

a. Imagine a wall. ☐
b. Make a square hole in the wall. ☐
c. Fill in the hole with glass. ☐

What does it look like now? _____

CHECK: Read sentences **a, b,** and **c** again. Did you imagine <u>all</u> the changes?

Underline the word or words that make each sentence go with the picture. Then print that word in the blank.

1. The dog's bone is

_____

    beside   under   in

the hole in the ground.

2. The old car is always

_____

    in in front of over

the house.

Read the story. Then answer each question **yes** or **no.** Finally, follow the directions to show that your answer is right.

Crickets are insects that look like short, fat grasshoppers. Male crickets make a chirping sound. Female crickets do not make a chirping sound. But both male and female crickets go out for food at night.

1. Do crickets look like grasshoppers? _____
   Copy the sentence from the story that tells you. □

   _____

   _____

2. Do male crickets make a chirping sound? _____
   Copy the sentence from the story that tells you. □

   _____

   _____

3. Do female crickets make a chirping sound? _____
   Copy the sentence from the story that tells you. □

   _____

   _____

CHECK: Read each sentence you copied. Does it show that your answer is right?

Read each sentence, and look at each picture. Circle the word in each sentence that is wrong. Then print a better word above it.

1. The eagle wore a large wig on its head. ☐

2. Ruth held some flowers in her teeth. ☐

CHECK: Read each sentence the new way. Does it go with the picture?

Read the pair of sentences. Then complete the second sentence to tell why the first sentence is silly.

The fish swam with its fins in its pockets.

Fish don't have _____. ☐

CHECK: Read the sentence you completed. Is it true? Does it tell what's wrong with the first sentence of the pair?

Underline the best word to complete each sentence.
Then print that word in the blank.

1. Eva fed _____ to the birds. ☐
   drums   crumbs   tigers

2. Vince hates the ticking of his
   _____. ☐
   clothes   clock   sister

3. _____ keep your coat closed. ☐
   Buttons   Sleeves   Gloves

4. Poppy ran so _____ that she
   quickly   loudly   slowly
   lost the race. ☐

5. I hurt myself when I dropped
   the _____ on my foot. ☐
   feather   rock   pencil

6. _____ don't have any legs. ☐
   Snakes   Spiders   Birds

CHECK: Read each completed sentence. Does it make
sense? Does the word you chose sound right with the
rest of the sentence?

*Determining meaning from context: Using context before, after, or around a blank

1. Look at the picture. Then read the story, and underline the words that tell about <u>three</u> things the artist forgot to draw. Do not underline anything else.

> Hallie is building a snowman. The two rocks in Hallie's hands are going to be the snowman's eyes. Right now, the snowman is wearing sunglasses. They look just like the sunglasses that Hallie is wearing. The snowman's smile is made of other rocks.

2. Now add to the picture the things you underlined.

Read the pair of sentences. Then complete the second sentence to tell why the first sentence is silly.

Howard was surprised when the wings and wheels fell off his car.

A car doesn't have _____. ☐

1. First read this story.

> If smoke and fog get mixed together, we call it smog. Smog happens most often in cities. Too much smog can hurt people, plants, animals, and buildings. Most cities are trying to control their smog.

2. Now underline the sentence or the words in the story that answer each question below. Then copy the words you underlined onto the blanks.

Where can you find smog? ☐

_____

_____

Why don't people like smog? ☐

_____

_____

Mark the sentence that answers the question.

What animal eats tree leaves? ☐

_____ The giraffe eats plants and tree leaves.

_____ The giraffe and zebra live in Africa.

Index

(Boldface entries are test pages.)